Love Is...

First edition 2022
Published by Three Horse Publishing

ISBN: 978-1-7370732-4-6

THREE HORSE
PUBLISHING

LOVE

is ...

by Leah Vis

LOVE

is patient

and kind

LOVE
does not envy

LOVE
does not brag

LOVE

is not

arrogant

LOVE
is not rude

LOVE
is not selfish

LOVE
is not
irritable

LOVE

is not
resentful

LOVE
is not happy
when things
go wrong

LOVE

celebrates

honesty

LOVE protects

LOVE
trusts

LOVE
stays hopeful

LOVE
doesn't give up

LOVE never ends!

Inspired by 1 Corinthians 13:4-8

Made in the USA
Las Vegas, NV
08 January 2024

84099011R00021